Judy FOR GIRLS 1990

W9-CEW-485

£3.10

The Christmas Spirit

SHIRLEY GREEN was the spoilt only child of wealthy parents. One Christmas Eve she met her cousin, Carol, whose family was not nearly so well off.

No, I certainly *DON'T* want to go to your little youth club disco tomorrow. It sounds so dreary.

Oh! Suit yourself then, Shirley. Er — are you coming carol-singing with us beforehand? It's to raise money for the Children's Home.

What? And miss all those special TV shows? These charities get enough money anyway.

Soon after—

That belt is just the thing I need to brighten up my old outfit for the disco — but I've only got fifty pence.

Spare something for the Old Folk's Treat, girls?

Er — I've no change.

Certainly!

Thanks a lot. Merry Christmas!

More fool you, Carol! I know that was all the money you had.

Well, it was a good cause — and it IS Christmas!

Christmas! Huh! Just an excuse for begging! Now you don't even have your bus fare home. See you, Carol.

That belt IS rather nice. I think I'll buy it for myself.

PARTY TIME

GIFTS

£12.50

At home that evening—

"A Christmas Carol". What's that about, Mother?

A CHRISTMAS CAROL

It's one of my favourite stories. This old miser, Scrooge, is taught a lesson by three ghosts . . .

As the story unfolded—

That's the Ghost of Christmas Past. He takes Scrooge back to his younger days.

Then—

The Ghost of Christmas Yet to Come?

Yes, dear. The ghost shows Scrooge what will happen if he doesn't change his mean ways.

Later—

I think I'll go to bed. I feel a bit queasy.

Too many mincemeat pies, I suggest, young lady! You'll be better in the morning. Goodnight, dear.

Maybe I HAVE eaten too many mincemeat pies. I can't seem to get to sleep.

Finally, Shirley fell asleep — only to dream—

I am the Ghost of Christmas Yet to Come!

Suddenly, she awoke with a start—

I must have left my door open — and I hear voices! Who can it be at this time of night?

Funny! The house seems different somehow. And that picture wasn't on the wall when I went to bed!

No, I *DON'T* want to support your charity! There should be a law against you carol singers disturbing the neighbourhood.

TRINGG!

Good riddance — Oh, no! The bell again!

Can't you take a telling? Oh! It's you! What do you want?

We came to invite you to our home for Christmas. It's no time to be on your own. And here's your Christmas present.

You'd better come in, I suppose. I got your card. I — I'm not sending any this year. Don't believe in it.

What a horrible woman! Yet there's something familiar about her. Who is she — and why does nobody seem to see me?

You'll want tea, I dare say. Wait in here.

I don't know why you persist in visiting your awful cousin every Christmas, dear. She gets meaner and more like Scrooge every year. Not even a Christmas decoration!

Shirley can't help it. She's lived here on her own since her parents died. Lonely people can get like that.

Shirley? Could it be . . .?

7

9

The Personal Touch

Here are some cheap and easy to make gifts. They'd make ideal presents for Mum or Gran — and you can personalise them too.

LAVENDER BAG

You'll need one piece of white net fabric measuring 36 cm. by 15 cm., one piece of pastel coloured satin cut to exactly the same size, one metre of satin ribbon measuring 5 mm. wide and a little dried lavender.

Pin the net fabric to the right side of the satin and then fold it in half, with the net sides together, thus forming a rectangle 18 cm. by 15 cm. Next, stitch down the sides of the rectangle leaving a gap of 5 mm., some 5 cm. from the open end of the rectangle. Turn over a double hem at this end. Then make two rows of stitching (5 mm. apart) across the rectangle, in line with the break in the seam, thus forming a channel though which you can thread the satin ribbon.

To personalise, cut out the required initial from felt material and stick it on using material glue.

PRETTY POMANDER

Chose a ripe, thick skinned orange and, starting from the stalk, work around the orange sticking it with cloves. Continue until the orange is completely covered. Then, tie a ribbon securely around the orange and make a loop at the top for hanging.

THE EGG COSY

To make this egg cosy all you need is one small piece of material 16 cm. square, a length of fancy lace, a small piece of felt for the initial and some material glue.

Lay a 15 cm. saucer on your material, draw round it, and cut out a circle. Fold the material in half and cut along the straight edge. Fold back the straight edges to make a small hem. Put the right sides of material together and place the ribbon or lace into the centre of the circle. Sew around the rounded edge making sure that you catch all three pieces. Turn outside in. To complete the egg cosy, cut the initial you want out of the felt and glue it on to one side.

HOME COOKING

Sally put the cake in a plastic bag and sneaked off.

I'll never live it down if the others see this cake! I must get rid of it somehow! Good job Miss Robbins wants me to pop into town for her.

Sally Smith! It *is* Sally, isn't it?

Are you feeling OK? I mean, you're all bent over!

Oh! I'm fine, really! Er, excuse me!

Nearly dropped the dratted cake I'm hiding under the back of my jacket!

I didn't know 3A were doing the Hunchback of Notre Dame for Open Day! I thought it was King Lear!

Outside, Sally met the school gardener.

Hi, Mr Brown! Haven't seen you this last couple of days.

No, been having some trouble with my new teeth. All right now, though.

At the bus stop—

Not a soul about. I'll leave the horrid cake here and get the bus.

Hey, you went straight past!

I suppose he didn't see me. Oh, well — just have to walk, I suppose. I'll take the short-cut up past the library.

12

14

THE END

20

A PONY has a near (left) and an off (right) side. Most of the handling of ponies — and especially leading — is done from the left-hand side. Working from the nearside it's called. However, a pony should also get used to being led from his offside, for this is useful when riding one pony and leading another.

A pony that naps is a menace, because it means he is rebellious and possibly dangerous. Nappy ponies need re-schooling and a very firm rider who is able to push him on with legs applied firmly, often behind the girth. Even the use of a riding whip may be needed to enforce obedience. Such a pony should never be bought for a novice rider, otherwise it will take advantage of the owner's inexperience, which could lead to an accident.

PONY

Nappy ponies often try scraping off the rider by jamming her/his leg against a gatepost. They may barge into other ponies deliberately, do their best never to leave stable/field if a companion is left behind, and play up in traffic.

22

pony with a vice is one that chases people and other ponies, trying to bite or kick them. This is called savaging. No pony used for children should have any vices at all.

An experienced rider may be able to handle such a mean-natured beast, but she would have to ride alone to prevent damage to other people and ponies. A pony that suddenly develops a vice needs checking by the vet, as there could be something causing pain that makes the animal resent being handled, bridled, or ridden.

LANGUAGE

A pony that is not up to weight is too fine and lightly-built to be able to carry a heavy rider — for example, a 10-stone girl on a half thoroughbred. An 8 — 8½ stone rider would be ideal.

Never buy a pony without first having it examined by a vet. He will test it for soundness and advise you of any problems.

A pony that is unsound may have a variety of things wrong with it. Unsoundness can stand for any of the following: — lameness; shortage of breath with a panting movement of the flanks, called "Broken Wind"; an eye defect — being partly-sighted in one or both eyes; heart problem; mouth problem — for example, "Parrot Mouthed", where the upper jaw overlaps the bottom jaw, making it difficult for the pony to eat properly.

23

GIRLS WHO WEAR GLASSES....

GINA BARBER was a pupil at Dinworth Comprehensive. Although she tried hard in class, Gina often had problems reading the blackboard as she had very poor eyesight.

So now you can see the answer quite clearly.

Well I jolly well can't.

These notes should help you, Gina.

Thanks, Natalie.

I wish you'd wear your glasses, Gina.

Stop going on, Natalie. I don't really need them!

Hey, that was Alan Beadle!

What? Oops! I didn't see that waste-paper basket.

Later—

It's not fair. Alan just doesn't seem to notice me.

I'm sure he does, Gina. You'll just have to be patient. See you tomorrow.

That red dress is gorgeous. I bet Alan would notice me in that if I wore it to the disco.

It's Alan! With Deirdre Summerton! I'd know that floppy blonde hair anywhere. Crumbs! No wonder he's never bothered about me.

What a dope I am. Fancy imagining he could ever be interested in me anyway.

Be just like me to miss my stop without these. What's it they say? 'Boys never make passes at girls who wear glasses'.

Next day—

Oh, it's him. Don't panic, Gina.

Do you realise that Alan has just turned round at the end of the corridor and is staring back at you?

Don't be silly, Natalie.

You know fine he is — why are you ignoring him?

Because he's already got a girlfriend. I don't want to talk about it actually.

Later, at lunch break—

He doesn't even know I exist!

It's him. Well, I can be sure that he's not looking for me.

Later—

Honestly, Natalie, everywhere I go I see him. It's uncanny.

Maybe he does fancy you after all.

I'm just kidding myself. Alan won't fancy me in a million years.

ALL THE WORLD'S A STAGE . . .

Can you complete this verse, Gina?

Complete it? I can't even READ it.

Er — um — no, sorry, Miss Deevers.

You COULD have, if you'd been paying attention. Go to the library and look up the quotation. Maybe then you'll remember it.

Let's see . . . Shakespeare. That's the top shelf on the left.

26

The End

27

Bobby Dazzler

BOBBY DAZZLER was the only girl at Westbury Boarding School for Boys, where her mother was Matron. One day, the Head introduced a friend of his, a writer of children's plays, to the newly-formed drama group.

And Miss Lorna Long is kindly allowing us to put on one of her unpublished plays for the local children's hospital.

Oh, great! Kids love stories about pirates and stuff.

I'll be Redbeard, terror of the Carribean!

Oh, no you won't! *I* write for little kiddie-widdies of three and four. Now, let me see . . . I think you two would be perfect as the two bunnie-wunnies.

BUNNIE-WUNNIES?

OH, NO!

If Miss Long says you're to be — er — bunnie-wunnies, then you're to be bunnie-wunnies.

But, sir . . .

31

I've got to get back before their taxi leaves!

Isn't that Bobby behind us? Shall we stop?

STOP!

We can't, we're a bit late as it is. The show must go on . . . she'll understand.

By the time Bobby reached the Town Hall she was too late—

This way, please, miss.

TOWN HALL

THE

JU

No, thanks all the same. I — I think I'll wait for my friends outside.

Meanwhile, the boys had arrived with only minutes to spare—

AUD

You're on. But — but, I . . .

We're late!

The boys went straight into their act—

Well, here we are again, Floppity . . . tell me, why have humans got such funny ears?

Well, Flippety, I think it's because . . . because . . . oh, no!

D-do you see what I see?

I see it, Mike. And — and you know what I'm thinking?

Boy bunnies with red faces. What a hoot!

JUDO COMPETITION

THE SIR JOHN TALENT JUDO COMPETI

OWN HALL

I tried! I really tried! But, maybe they won't see it that way! Think I'll just make my way home on my own.

THE END

32

NIGHT OF THE CAT

. . . while you just lie here, cosy and warm! I wish I had your life!

Sandra didn't know how long she'd been lying there . . .

Sandra — your supper's ready!

I must have fallen asleep! Oh, no — I haven't tidied up yet!

I'd better go down . . . Oh, something's terribly wrong!

Lyn came upstairs.

Sandra? Oh, all right — I'll just let you sleep on while Ben and I eat.

That's Kitty that Lyn is talking to — and this is me!

Downstairs—

Sandra can have her supper later, Ben. Now, I wish I hadn't shouted at her.

I'm starving! Oh, I know what to do . . .

Just look at Kitty! It's as if she's trying to get a saucer!

Poor thing! She must be thirsty!

34

Here you are, puss.

This milk is better than nothing, I suppose. I just hope I can manage to lap it up properly the way Kitty does!

Suddenly—

Sandra! What are you doing with the goldfish?

Stop that!

Yes — put the fish back at once, Sandra!

I think she's acting up because Mum and Dad are away. I'll go up and talk to her after I've washed the dishes. Will you put the cat out?

Go to bed!

Miaooooow!

What did she say?

What's come over Sandra?

Out?

Out here all night? What will I do when it gets dark? I'm not sure Kitty has such a good life after all!

Miaow!

Kitty must have sneaked out — and she's talking cat language! Perhaps that means I can still talk human language, even if I'm in the body of a cat!

And so she could.

Don't cry, Kitty. I know how frightened you must be, but we're in this together.

For a moment, the cat and the girl comforted each other.

Then—

Here comes that horrible boy who always pulls Kitty's tail!

Too late to hide! Here, give me that stupid cat!

Go away, you big bully!

Aaaaah!

The c-cat can speak! I'm getting away from here — and I'm not coming back!

37

HORSES and RIDERS

YOU might feel good on a large horse, but it isn't safe. If you are small, you could never hold such a strong animal should it take fright and bolt. A too-light rider, often inexperienced, could be seriously hurt. Even if this doesn't happen, she is likely to haul on the horse's mouth, or let the horse have its own way. The first hurts the horse, often resulting in it becoming one-sided, responding only to one rein for the rest of its life because of damage to the nerves in the mouth. The second leads, in a short time, to the animal becoming uncontrollable and a menace to other horses.

There is no accurate weight-for-age guide for riders, since people grow according to their bone structure. Nor is there a height-of-horse for riders' height guide, because some slightly-built horses can only carry a lightweight rider, whereas a strong, cobby pony will carry a man six feet tall. However, it is not wise to ride a large animal, no matter how quiet to handle and well-behaved it may be, when a smaller one will suit you better.

Some shows and gymkhanas are partly to blame. They restrict the rider by age instead of ability. Thus a sixteen-year-old turns up on a 15.3 hands horse because the class says: "Horses up to 16 hands; riders 16 or over." Such a rider may be under five feet four inches in height, weigh about eight stones, and be there only for the ride! The showring is full of horses that have been corned up all winter, schooled to perfection to win. Like all horses, they know when riders are too small to handle them properly, and take advantage of that.

38

You simply can't push a massive 16 hands horse on into his stride if your heels barely come below the saddle flap. Nor can you steady him at a jump when he is pulling like a train. One jerk can have you out of the saddle and clinging to his neck.

To judge, roughly, the height of horse or pony suited to height of rider, sit astride the animal bareback, letting your legs hang loose. Your feet should be midway between the horse's elbow and his knee.

Horses are fine for adults, but they don't take kindly to being squeezed through small gateways into gardens or paddocks, or through gaps in hedges leading to bridleways or lanes. They play up when they aren't sufficiently exercised or are overfed. Ponies are best for lighter weight riders. They're nippier movers, too, which is why so many of them are winners in gymkhana games. They are less excitable, less prone to injuries, and cost less to keep.

What's more, if you can ride a pony of about 13 to 13.2 hands really well and care for it properly summer and winter, the knowledge gained will benefit you when you have grown into riding a horse. So get the learning — and falling off — done on the smaller steed before graduating to a horse. It's a long drop to the ground!

AND REMEMBER —
ALWAYS WEAR A
PROPER RIDING HAT
TO PROTECT YOUR
HEAD.

LOST ON THE MOOR

But Papa's so strict, Thomas. Nothing more than a lady-like canter, and always a groom with me.

JENNY loved more than anything to ride out on the moors. She wanted to gallop and gallop, free as the wind.

The master's right, Miss Jenny. It isn't fitting for a young lady to ride out alone.

Oh, really, Thomas! This is 1790, not the Middle Ages. Times change, you know.

Your father doesn't change, miss. And we'll have to stop a minute. I think old Roger's losing a shoe.

You stay with Roger, then — Star and I are going for a gallop!

MISS JENNY!

Faster . . . faster, Star . . . there's no one to stop us now! Oh, this is wonderful!

At last, horse and rider drew to a breathless halt —

I did enjoy that, Star. We'll rest here a while, then go back to Thomas. I — I just hope he doesn't tell tales about me to Papa.

Already Jenny was beginning to feel guilty —

Thomas is bound to tell Papa. I suppose we'd better start back now, and get the scolding over with.

But Jenny couldn't find the place where she'd left Thomas —

It was near a big patch of gorse bushes . . . but I can't see him anywhere. I-I do believe I'm lost!

It's growing quite dark. I'd better stay dismounted in case Star stumbles.

The darkness came down on the moor like a heavy blanket —

I — can't see where I'm going . . . I daren't walk another step. Oh, wait! There's a light ahead . . . oh, thank goodness!

Oh, please, whoever you are, help me! I'm lost!

Don't be afraid. Keep on calling, to guide me to you.

Soon —

If — if you could just lead me to the road . . . I must get back to my family.

Follow me . . . hold onto my sleeve. I know this moor, even in the dark.

What is she doing, wandering about the moor in the dark? And what strange clothing she wears!

There is the road, just ahead. You're safe now.

Thank you so much! My name is Jenny Haverly. If you are ever near Haverly Hall, come in and take tea with us. I must go now — my family will be worried.

I must go, too . . . before my lamp goes out.

Goodbye, Jenny.

The girl with the lantern pushed open the door of a farmhouse nearby.

Marian, why were you so long? I only sent you to get wood for the fire.

I heard a lost girl calling. I showed her the way to Haverly Hall.

And will someone PLEASE remember to put a battery in the torch? It went out before I could get the wood — and there was hardly any oil in the old lantern.

Why don't YOU remember to put it in? You're not helpless, are you?

Here, the battery's in now. Charlie, you go and get the wood, will you? I want Marian to help me with the supper.

Oh . . . alright, Mum.

42

CHRIS JOHNSON worked at a residential nursery for the under-fives. One morning . . .

JUNIOR NANNY

Nurse Chris, my teddy's been stolen!

I expect one of the other children has just borrowed him, Becky. Come along, and we'll ask them.

Two-year-old Bobby was the culprit —

Teddy very tired. Bobby put him to bed.

Where, Bobby? Show me.

Put teddy in box. Ooh! Teddy gone!

The dustmen came about ten minutes ago! You might catch them!

WAIT!

There's just a chance they spotted the teddy.

I just chucked the box in with the other rubbish, Nurse. I'm sorry.

Oh, no! Becky will be so disappointed!

Next morning, at the local hospital —

Hello, Sister Hughes. Nurse Chris said you wanted to see me.

Yes, dear. I am so sorry about your poor teddy. Becky, do you remember Doctor Teddy?

Oh, yes, Sister! I called him the second best teddy in the world. Doctor Teddy helps sick little girls and boys.

That's right, dear. Now we are going to give him to *YOU*.

I can't take Doctor Teddy away! The sick girls and boys need him!

Nurse Chris and I will leave you for a while, to think about it. Talk to Doctor Teddy—ask his advice.

Ten minutes later —

Doctor Teddy and me had a chat. He told me to try to love another teddy bear, so I will, to please him.

Becky wanted the new teddy bear from the dustmen to belong to all the nursery children —

I'd like to have your old teddy, Nurse Chris, please, 'cos you loved him and I love you. Doctor Teddy thinks I'll be kind to your teddy.

I'm sure Doctor Teddy is right, Becky.

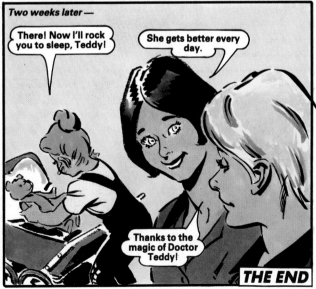

Two weeks later —

There! Now I'll rock you to sleep, Teddy!

She gets better every day.

Thanks to the magic of Doctor Teddy!

THE END

Saturday Date

IT all started when Sally got off on the wrong foot at her new school. Her aunt, one of the teachers, gave her a lift.

Look at that — another teacher's pet. She needs taking down a peg or two!

SALLY

PAUL

Lily's got that look in her eye. That new kid had better watch out.

JIMMY

HUGH

A few weeks later, good-looking Paul Tippet spoke to Sally —

Sally, have you got a date for the school disco on Saturday?

Why, no, Paul, I haven't.

She felt her face redden as Bobby walked off —

Strange! He's just walking away!

I haven't dated much, it's true, so maybe I don't know how it works. But shouldn't he have asked me to go with him?

Sally consulted Annie Foster, a girl who'd helped her on her first day —

What — what's going on here? Is it something I'm doing wrong?

Annie, if some boy asked you if you had a date for the Saturday disco and you said "no", what would you expect him to do?

Why, ask me to go with him, of course.

Later, Bobby Newton whispered in her ear—

Are you fixed up for the school disco?

No, Bobby, I'm not.

Sally told Annie about Paul and Bobby—

I thought so. Lily Lee's lot. They've got it in for you — I suppose because of your aunt. Look, Sally, the next one that asks, say you've got a date.

All right, Annie, I suppose that's the best way.

The next one to ask was Jimmy Jackson—

Yes, Jimmy, thank you for your interest, but I'm fixed up.

Oh!

She told Annie what had happened—

But what do I do now? When I don't turn up on Saturday they'll know I was fibbing.

I wish I could help you, but I can't be there. Look, Sally, just turn up at the disco.

It's always so crowded, they'll never notice you're on your own. It's what I'd do.

Where will it all end? I ask myself. Where will it all end?

No, I don't believe it. COOK'S trying for a part now!

Just see this list, Nellie. Twenty-four we'll be having to dinner for this new-fangled rehearsal.

If that includes Mr Salinger, you'd better make it twenty-seven! He eats like a horse!

In the drawing room —

So it's your opinion that this uprising in the colonies will soon be put down then, sir?

That it will, Sir William, that it will. You can take that as gospel. From the horse's mouth, so to speak. Yessir.

Oh, Mr Salinger, how very knowledgeable you are, to be sure.

But one can see that reflected in the beautiful dialogue of "Christmas At The Palace" Oh, yes indeed!

Thank YOU, ladies. I must admit in all modesty I have yet to see my plays bettered either side of the Atlantic.

And the role of the Princess Caroline. I feel I know her so well. It's as if I, myself, knew her every thought.

Oh, sister! Those were my very words to you upon rising this morning!

Girls! Girls! I feel sure your dear mama has need of you in the conservatory!

But, Papa . . .

Dear Mr Salinger hasn't even heard us READ yet!

And how that emerald green velvet does become you, Lady Fitzhowlan.

You jest, my lord. I have promised the last minuet to the Honourable Toby Provence.

My ladies are still rehearsing. I'd better get this holly inside double quick, before they start arguing!

But —

I'm quite sure the Princess Caroline would never be seen in a chapeau like THAT!

Sister, that plum colour does NOTHING for your complexion!

Ladies, please! This holly is really very prickly . . .

Later—

Oh, fie sir, you flatterer!

PLEASE, my dear, I have some papers to attend to. Go somewhere else and rehearse.

LAWKS!

Ow! I reckon this play is doing me more mischief than anyone else in this house!

I am quite happy now. The part of the queen is just made for me! Victoria — such a SEEMLY name.

I always SAID Princess Caroline was the part for me. Oh, Nellie, do try and make yourself presentable for the rehearsal. Smarten yourself up.

56

Smarten myself up? Huh!

In the kitchen—

Oh, sir, I'm afraid you must have mistaken your way . . .

No, no! Just feeling a mite peckish, ma'am. Those pastries smell delicious!

Reminds me of old Topsy's kitchen back in Saskatchewan. Ah, caraway buns. I have to compliment you, Cook.

Well actually, Nellie here's responsible for those, sir.

Thank you, Nellie. I feel refreshed enough now to cast my last role.

But we'll BOTH be responsible if her ladyship catches Mr Salinger in the kitchen. Coo, Americans certainly ARE different!

His last role? But what about Flora and Alice and Lady Selby Smythe? Lawks! Whoever he chooses, there's bound to be a right royal scene with the other two!

Yessir, I think we might say the casting is almost complete. The queen and the two princesses will be played by the most professional actresses of the theatre, of course. I know the ladies well.

Oh!

That still leaves the titled ladies of the court to be cast.

Swans 'n' things
★ FUN TO MAKE ★

SOUVENIR SHOWCASE

Glue boxes of different shapes and sizes together, starting with really stout ones at the base. Before gluing, twist the boxes to different angles, as you see in the drawing. Paint or cover the outside of the boxes in one colour, so that it is the contents that catch the eye. Richly-coloured interiors, however, can be very attractive.

SCENTED SWAN

Cut four discs of stiffish, non-fray material, each 8 cm. in diameter. Glue two together round the edge (1), leaving a 6 cm. gap. Add one disc on each side (2) gluing lightly at edges and front and back. Bend a pipe cleaner to the pattern (left) and glue in place (see big pic). Moisten a pad of cotton-wool with perfume and place in the gap arrowed (2).

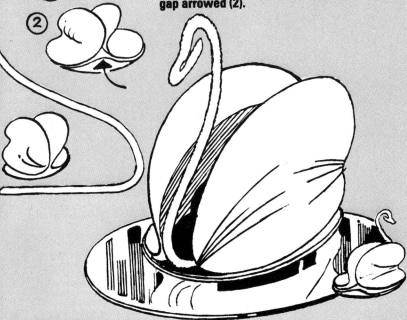

TIDY TRAY

Cut a loo roll into three parts (1), then wind with wool gluing the ends down (2). Cut a card disc to fit the top of each and bind with wool (3). Hinge on with stitches. Decorate the tubs by sewing contrasting wool through every three rows. Cut a 12 cm. diameter disc from thick card for the base then a 10 cm. length from the outer case of a discarded ballpoint pen (4) and glue to the disc (5). Add a large bead to the rod, finally gluing the tubs to the base.

"JUDY" FILE

Ideal for keeping your fave mag clean and tidy on the bookshelf. Make from corrugated sandwich board to the dimensions below. Just fold into shape, then secure it with a strip of sticky tape along the bottom.

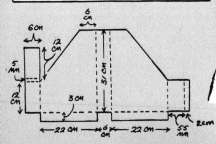

HANDY PAD

Use thickish card to cut out the shape shown, score and bend on the dotted lines, and glue down the tabs. Decorate by pasting on pretty paper, or painting with poster colours. Cut paper to size, fill it up, and it's ready

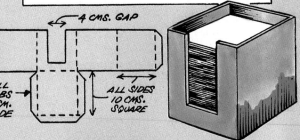

Cinderella Jones

CINDY JONES worked hard for her keep at the Happyholme Guest House, Brightsea, owned by her stepmother, while her stepsisters, Isobelle and Sarah, did nothing. Her father, a travelling salesman, was at home just before Christmas.

Would you like to see what I've bought your stepmother for Christmas, Cindy?

A string of pearls! Dad, they're beautiful!

We're going to the hoteliers' ball on Boxing Day. Agnes has always wanted to outdo that snobby Mrs Smithers.

I'm sure Stepmother will impress everyone with these, Dad! I'll wrap them up for you.

I'm off for a business trip, Cindy, and I may not be back until Christmas Day. Could you put Agnes's gift under the tree with the other presents?

Sure, Dad. Don't forget to put some kisses on that gift card.

'Bye, Dad!

Here's the coal lorry. At least we'll not be cold at Happyholme this Christmas.

Don't stand out there idling your time away, Cindy! I want the entire house cleaned from top to bottom for Christmas!

Just coming, Stepmother.

In the dining room—

How about joining in the festive spirit and giving me a hand, you two?

We can't, Cindy. We're decorating the tree.

Yes, decorating the tree.

The following day, the guests began to put presents under the tree—

Christmas Eve, Cindy! I can hardly wait for midnight when we can all open our presents.

And no peeking before then, eh, ladies?

Later—

Oh, no! Coal dust has blown out from under the cellar door. I'll have to clean up the hall again!

Mother, you mustn't! You're supposed to wait until midnight!

Yes, midnight!

Hello — Isobelle, Sarah and Stepmother. What ARE they up to?

Pearls, Mother! They're beautiful!

Yes, beautiful!

But are they REAL?

She's biting the pearls to see if they're real! OOOOOH!

61

Wrap up the empty box again or Cindy might get suspicious.

Now what's she going to do?

That afternoon, Mrs Jones and Cindy went shopping—

You can go home now, Cindy. I have a bit of special shopping to do.

Stepmother told me she'd bought all the presents, so what's she up to?

Cindy just had to find out—

She must be having Dad's gift valued! What a sneaky, ungrateful thing to do!

Later, at home—

There she goes to put Dad's pearls back into the box now the jeweller's told her they're real. She needs taught a lesson — and I think I know how!

That evening, Cindy took Mr Jones' gift from under the tree—

I'll switch Dad's pearls for some of my old plastic beads.

Midnight came—

Thanks, Mrs Leyton. Just what I wanted.

This is my present from Arnold. I wonder *WHAT* he can have bought me?

Socks! Lovely!

My goodness — I do believe it's jewellery!

Now for it!

EEEEEK!

Mrs Jones! What's the matter?

My pearls! Somebody's taken my pearls and left me plastic beads! Nobody leave the room! Isobelle — call the police!

I'd better fetch the pearls and put her out of her misery.

It was bad enough opening Dad's present before midnight, Stepmother, but to actually have it valued . . . You don't deserve these!

I might have known you'd be at the back of this, Cindy!

Give them here!

Be careful, Stepmother! *NOW* look what you've done! The string's broken!

Stop them! My pearls! My beautiful pearls!

They're bouncing into the coal! Oh, no!

Some time later—

I'm home! Merry Christmas, everybody . . .

Hello? Where ARE they all?

I don't care if it takes all night! I want all of them found!

I've sifted through that lot! Here's one! And here's another! Hand me the shovel, Cindy!

Hi, Dad. Is that another present for me?

Y-yes, Cindy . . . what on earth are you all doing down there!

My pearls! My beautiful pearls!

SOAP, Dad! Just what I wanted!

MERRY CHRISTMAS, EVERYBODY!

MERRY CHRISTMAS!

The End

A Package For Paula

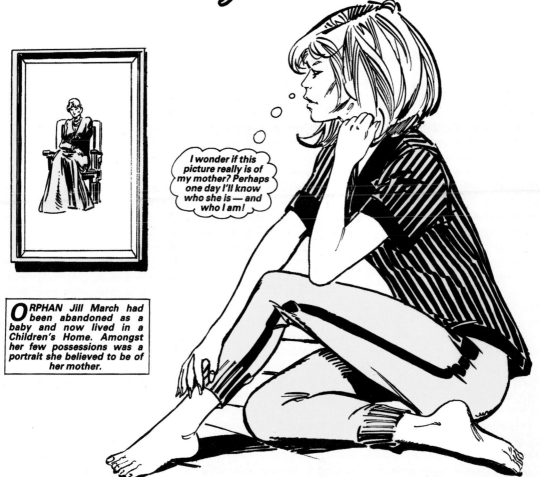

ORPHAN Jill March had been abandoned as a baby and now lived in a Children's Home. Amongst her few possessions was a portrait she believed to be of her mother.

I wonder if this picture really is of my mother? Perhaps one day I'll know who she is — and who I am!

Two days later, Mrs Clay, the matron of the Children's Home, asked Jill to run an errand for her—

This package was delivered here from the bank by mistake. It's addressed to someone called Paula Langham. Will you take it back, Jill?

Of course, Mrs Clay.

So, later at the bank—

This was delivered in error. There's no one of this name at the Home.

I see . . . That's most peculiar. Are you POSITIVE there's no Paula Langham there?

Quite sure, I'm afraid.

We received precise instructions to deliver the package to her at that address. It's been in our strong room for years.

In fact, the owner has paid for this to be kept here for well over ten years. Yesterday we received a letter telling us to deliver it to the Children's Home. The owner is only identified by a box number. Would you mind keeping the package at the Home for the moment? Paula Langham may turn up to collect it.

All right — I'll take it back and give it to Matron to lock away.

A few days later, the Children's Home had a visit from the local councillor, Mrs Harding —

I hope you don't mind my dropping in. This is my new secretary, Paula.

PAULA? Could it be?

When Mrs Harding left, her secretary hung back—

Mrs Clay, has a package addressed to me, Paula Langham, arrived here recently?

YOU'RE Paula Langham? Yes . . . it has. We were wondering about it. I'll fetch it from the safe.

It's some jewellery that belonged to my late mother. I couldn't have it sent home, or my stepmother would have claimed it.

And you knew you'd be coming here with Mrs Harding and could pick it up! Well, I'm glad you've got it now, my dear.

The following week, Jill was in town again—

TEA HOUSE

There's Paula Langham, Mrs Harding's secretary!

Hello, Paula! How are you?

Who are YOU?

The two girls hurried away—

She called you "Paula", Brenda!

I know she recognised me! And her friend called her "Brenda"! Something's not right! I'll go and ask Mrs Harding, the councillor, about her.

So, at the town hall—

Paula? Don't talk to me about HER! She walked out on me after only two days! I was so desperate for some help I didn't bother to check her references. She only started the morning I brought her to the Home.

Looks like she only took the job to have an excuse to visit the Home!

When Jill told her about the mysterious package, Mrs Harding called the police—

That's the girl! She's coming out of the office building she went into earlier!

Follow her at a safe distance. We'll see where she goes.

The girl met a young man outside the bank—

That's the cashier I told about the package and how there was no Paula Langham at the Home.

Obviously her boyfriend. Time to pick them up, Constable.

Back at the police station the two young people confessed—

The boyfriend knew the package must be valuable, so he persuaded the girl to impersonate this Paula Langham and collect it.

She applied to you, Mrs Harding, for a job, so that she'd have access to the Home. It could have worked, too, except that Jill spotted her, by chance, in the street.

POLICE

The package was recovered and the police 'phoned for Mrs Clay to collect Jill—

I feel very silly for having just handed over the package to "Paula".

The gold ring and locket it contained are beautiful — AND very valuable.

But it still doesn't tell us who Paula Langham really is!

I think it does! May I borrow the jewellery?

The detective agreed and, on the way home—

Mrs Clay, do you really know who Paula Langham is?

I'm ALMOST sure. When we get back I'll know one way or the other.

Mrs Clay took out a photograph album —

We always photograph every child who comes here, in case relatives show up. This is your picture, on arrival here, and the date shows when you came here. That's why we gave you the surname "March".

Mrs Clay opened the locket—

Notice any similarity?

IT'S ME! IT'S ME!

Jill rushed up to her room with the locket—

So I must be Paula Langham! The OTHER picture in the locket is of the woman in the portrait. She must be my mother!

She must have left the package with the bank when she abandoned me. Now she's decided it's time I learned who I am. Perhaps it's the first step towards my being re-united with my mother!

The End

67

RIVALS

SHEILA BALLANTINE gave her pony a gentle squeeze with her legs and urged him into a canter. "Come on, Mickey," she whispered, and Mickey obligingly went into an easy canter along the disused railway embankment, whose grassgrown cinder track provided a perfect surface for his sturdy legs. Two figures on horseback appeared ahead of Sheila, and she reined Mickey back.

The two figures, both of whom she recognised as fellow members of the local Pony Club group, produced conflicting emotions in Sheila. Her eyes rested with pleasure on Robert Blake, son of a local farmer. His mount was a graceful bay mare, called Flame, whom Sheila had often admired, though not in quite the same way as she admired Robert. The second figure was a less welcome sight. Annabel Dobson, on her expensive Arab gelding, Jetset, was Robert's most constant companion and Sheila's self-appointed critic at the Pony Club meeting. Criticisms of her clothes, her style of riding and instructions on how to groom Mickey all flowed in unasked. Sheila paid little attention since Annabel's own expensive mount was kept at livery and she played no part in actually looking after him.

Annabel had somehow convinced herself that she was the world's expert on horses, and was anxious that others should benefit from her knowledge. Sheila could not altogether deny that Annabel was a tolerable rider — she'd won too many cups and rosettes in jumping and showing classes for that.

LATELY a new aspect had crept into the less than friendly relationship between the two girls — ever since Sheila had begun to show signs of boundless admiration for Robert and Flame.

Annabel now talked down to Sheila in Robert's presence and treated her as though she were a child, not to be taken seriously. This had come to a head last week, when Annabel had taken Sheila aside and practically warned her off.

"It's natural you should have a crush on Robert, Sheila. After all, he's very attractive — but you'll get over it. When I was your age, I had a crush on someone."

Sheila had tried to smile and shrug it off. This "when I was your age" stuff was all too familiar, and quite absurd in view of the fact that Annabel was less than eighteen months older than her and Robert was only two years her senior.

"I would hardly call it a crush," she replied. "Robbie's helping me to school Mickey."

"Don't call him Robbie!" Annabel snapped. "He can't stand it."

"I'm sorry. I didn't know," Sheila muttered.

But Annabel had gone on relentlessly.

"Half the girls in the Pony Club have had a crush on him at one time or another. He's so friendly they think he's taking a special interest in them. But he's like that with everyone."

SHEILA had felt enormously depressed after this interview. Perhaps she *had* been building on nothing — creating a romantic dream out of a few smiles and the fact that Robbie always seemed pleased to see her.

The three riders drew level and Sheila stopped as Robert reined in his bay mare. She could see that Annabel would have liked to ride past, but she, too, stopped. Mickey immediately began nibbling at the fresh hawthorn leaves in the hedge.

"Don't let him eat that!" Annabel commanded.

for ROBBIE

"Oh, he'll be all right," chipped in Robert, smiling at Sheila. "Old Mickey's got a stomach of iron, hasn't he, Sheila? He's not as delicate as Jetset."

"Oh well, don't say I didn't warn you," snapped Annabel.

"Are you going to Heddon Gymkhana on Saturday?" Sheila asked, to fill the awkward pause which followed.

"Of course we are," Annabel replied. "The Open Jumping should be easy for horses like Jetset and Flame."

"I was thinking of going in for some of the sports events too — you know, like the egg and spoon race," Robert said. "What about you, Sheila?"

"Yes, they're more my cup of tea," she replied.

"You know, you really ought to get yourself a decent horse," Annabel sneered, "then I expect stand a chance of winning something. I expect Jetset will walk away with the 'Best Turned Out Pony' as usual."

"I know Mickey's no show pony," Sheila defended him, "but even if he's not good at jumping he's quite handy at bending and that sort of thing."

"I bet he's marvellous at the sack race, too," Robert encouraged.

"Well, we *have* been practising," Sheila admitted.

"Come on, Robert, we can't stand here chatting all day — we'll be late for supper," snapped Annabel.

Annabel dug her heels in and set off at a canter down the cinder track. Robert followed suit, turning for a moment to smile at Sheila.

"See you at the gymkhana on Saturday!" were his parting words.

EACH evening that week Sheila rushed home from school, gobbled her tea and was off to saddle Mickey and put him through his paces. They practised "bending" through a line of garden canes Sheila had erected in his field, then the egg and spoon race, where Mickey learned to trot slowly alongside while Sheila went as fast as she could without toppling the egg.

The sack race was the hardest, but Mickey had learned to stop whenever Sheila fell over, which was pretty often at first. By the end of the week she could do it without falling at all, and Mickey seemed to enjoy taking part and understood what was expected of him.

When Saturday morning came, Sheila was up early, grooming Mickey till he shone. Mickey might not be entering for any of the showing classes, but Sheila wanted him to look as smart as possible and to give Annabel Dobson no excuse for her critical remarks.

When she arrived at the gymkhana, it was already in full swing, most of the showing and jumping events being already over. The pony sports would come later. She could see Annabel in the collecting ring, waiting for the jump-off in the Open Jumping. The first round had eliminated all but four competitiors who had got a clear round and were now going to compete over slightly raised fences. Sheila could see that Jetset already had several rosettes pinned to his bridle, and one of them was red, for a first. No doubt that was for the Best Turned Out Pony Annabel had been so sure of.

Robert and Flame had been eliminated and were outside the ring watching Annabel in the jump-off. Sheila's impulse was to join him but she stayed where she was.

Annabel won the jump-off with the only second clear round, executed in faultless style, and cantered out of the ring with her second red rosette. Sheila could not help admiring horse and rider as they flew effortlessly over each fence, though she felt that Jetset could have managed a clear round with a sack of potatoes on his back. The next moment she was hating herself for so ungenerous a thought.

T HE jumping over, the sports events began. Sheila forgot her worries and threw herself wholeheartedly into the Egg and Spoon race. Mickey trotted obediently alongside her and she was soon leading the field. Unfortunately she dropped the egg five yards from the finish, was overtaken by the girl behind, and came in second.

She won another second, and another blue rosette, in the Bending. As she trotted out of the ring, she was joined by Robert and Annabel.

"Well done, Sheila," Robert greeted her. "I thought of putting our names down for the sack race. What do you think?"

"Don't be silly, Robert — this sort of thing is kids' stuff. Anyway you need a team of three for the sack race and there are only two of us," Annabel added pointedly.

"You'll join us, won't you, Sheila?"

"I'd love to."

Robert jumped off Flame and ran to put their names down before Annabel could make further objection. In a moment he was back again.

"I've entered us for the three-legged race too, Annabel," he said.

Annabel did not reply.

The sack race looked like being a fiasco for Sheila's team. Although Robert, who went first, managed to finish his leg of the race in close second place, when he handed over to Annabel she was slow getting into the sack and, once started, she fell over so many times that they were soon trailing behind the rest of the field.

"I said it was kids' stuff," Annabel snarled as she handed over the sack to Sheila for the final leg. "That's the last time I take part in these stupid events. I've absolutely ruined my hairdo, and just *look* at my jodhpurs!"

Sheila closed her ears to Annabel's moaning behind her and concentrated on the hundred yards ahead. Her nearest rival was ten yards in front, but she encouraged Mickey into a trot and, leaning heavily on his bridle, soon managed to overtake first this and

then the next rival. There were two more bunched ahead, then the leader. They were over halfway to the finishing line!

Sheila increased the length of her hops and had soon drawn level with the girls in second and third places. One of them fell over and was out of the race, the other changed direction to avoid tripping over her and Sheila had drawn past. That just left a boy in the lead. Sheila strained every nerve. Then the boy heard her at his heels, looked back to see her gaining on him and his pony stopped. He tugged at its bridle and smacked it on the shoulder, but it was too late! Sheila had gone into the lead, and she and Mickey crossed the finishing line amidst a round of applause and claimed the red rosette for her team.

"You were terrific!" Robert enthused, throwing his arms round her as she came out of the ring and giving her a hug. "I just hope Annabel and I can keep it up in the three-legged race."

"I've already told you I've had quite enough of these babyish events," Annabel said icily. "I'm going to get a cup of tea, Robert. Coming?"

But Robert stayed put.

"We'd better get a move on," Sheila smiled. "They're lining up for the three-legged race now."

Sheila's leg was bound to Robert's and, before long, they were off.

T HE worst thing, Sheila found, was keeping your balance. But with faithful old Mickey trotting steadily on one side and Robert's arm firmly round her waist, they made good progress and reached the finishing line without mishap, just ahead of the rest of the field. On the far side of the line Robert tripped and they both fell laughing together.

"You and Mickey must have the rosette," he said..

"Oh, but we couldn't — it was your idea to go in for the race. You keep it, Robert, please."

"Flame and I will keep it on two conditions — that you'll come to the Pony Club Dance with me tonight, and that you'll call me Robbie from now on. Robert *is* rather formal."

"But I thought you didn't like people to call you Robbie. Annabel said you couldn't stand it."

"Never mind Annabel. Will you come?" he smiled.

"Oh, yes, Robbie — of course I will. But what about Annabel — won't she feel, well — you know . . ."

She felt too embarrassed to finish.

"Annabel and I are riding companions, that's all. Our families have been close for years, and everyone has sort of expected *us* to be close. But we're not really."

"Oh, I see."

"You *are* funny," he went on, "worrying about Annabel's feelings, when you know the last thing in the world *she'd* ever do is worry about yours."

"I'm sorry, Robbie," she replied briefly. "You must think me rather silly."

"Don't be sorry," he said softly, "that's what I like about you."

He turned to smile at Mickey and Flame who were rubbing noses.

"It looks as though Mickey and Flame are going to hit it off too."

The End

THE *GHOST* OF ARMLEY FELL

What a great day for a walk!

ONE sunny morning, in the Lake District, a girl was setting out for the day.

Let's see. Armley Fell is where I want to go.

MOORTON FELL — ARMLEY FELL

Just then—

I wonder what those hikers want?

HEY!

We're wondering if you've taken a wrong turn. That path leads to Armley Fell.

I know. That's where I want to go.

Minutes later —

Wow! The mist is dense now. It came down so suddenly! I can't see where I'm going!

I'm sure I'm lost. And it's so treacherous if you wander off the paths.

Then—

Hi! Are you okay?

OH! You gave me a fright! I thought I was alone up here!

Sorry — I didn't mean to frighten you.

That's okay. Could you give me directions? I'm not sure where I am.

You're getting dangerously close to a path called "North Leap" — and it's a sheer drop if you fall from there.

Oh!

73

I think this mist will stay all day now. It would be safer for you to go back down. Would you like me to show you the way?

Okay, thanks. My name's Gina, by the way. What's yours?

I'm Mike. Come on — the safest path's over here.

He's very sure-footed, even in the mist. He must be an experienced fell-walker.

And, before long—

We're through the mist now. It's nice to see the sun again.

And we're almost at the bottom. Can you find your own way from here?

Yes. But why? Where are you going, Mike?

I'm taking this path. It goes to the farm where I live.

I see. Goodbye then — and thanks!

I'm often on the fells. Maybe I'll see you again, Gina.

I hope so! Mike's really nice.

Gina walked on alone—

ARMLEY FELL

I'm back at the signpost now. Oh, there are those hikers I saw earlier.

Hi! Did you enjoy your walk?

74

Yes, thanks. I was a bit lost in the mist though, but a boy showed me the way down.

A boy? WHAT boy?

His name was Mike. He went that way.

I can't see him.

Are you sure it was a BOY, and not the GHOST we told you about?

Of course Mike wasn't a ghost! He is definitely a real person. But he walks quickly, that must be why he's out of sight now!

It sounds a bit odd to me. I think he could have been a ghost. Armley Fell is definitely haunted.

I know it is. But MIKE isn't the ghost. I know that — because I AM.

I died in an accident on the fell. I fell from "North Leap" — the path Mike talked about. That was twenty years ago. And, every year, on the anniversary of my death, I walk the fell again.

THE END

75

LAURA'S LESSON

LAURA HURD was enjoying a joke in her class but, as usual, it was at someone else's expense—

You should have seen Tess Trumper at the keep fit class last night! She looked like an elephant in a leotard!

Laura goes too far. And I don't think the other girls are really amused, either.

When Tess jumped, the whole building shook.

Oh, no! She's talking about me!

Later—

Laura's right, Liz. I'm so fat that I'm a joke.

Don't cry, Tess. Laura was just trying to be smart by showing off to an audience.

Next day—

Hey! Look at this!

SCHOOL PANTO TO BE PRODUCED
GIRL WANTED TO ASSIST ME IN PUTTING THE SHOW ON THE ROAD.
SEE: MISS WILSON, DRAMA HEAD.

You'd be good at that, Liz.

Yes, Liz, why don't you try?

It's "Liz" this, "Liz" that . . . they get on my nerves!

Just then—

What's all this? Do you fancy yourself as my assistant, Liz? Come and see me Saturday afternoon and we'll have a talk.

Thanks, Miss Wilson.

At the Riding Club on Saturday morning—

Is that a new horse?

Yes, this is Thunder. I wouldn't advise trying him yet. He's pretty temperamental.

I thought YOU were going to see Miss Wilson today!

Not until this afternoon, Laura. Plenty of time for a ride first.

This is Thunder, the new horse. Do you want to ride him?

I hope Thunder gives Liz a nasty fright. Then she might not make that appointment with Miss Wilson. Serve little Miss Clever Clogs right!

He looks superb! Coming for a canter, Thunder?

Steady, Thunder!

He seems nervous.

WOAH, THUNDER!

Oh, no . . . he's bucking!

Liz landed heavily—

Oh! I'm aching! That was mean of you, Thunder!

That afternoon—

Liz, what happened to your eye?

I fell off a horse this morning. It's nothing serious, Miss Wilson.

I'm glad it didn't stop you coming here today. You're obviously very reliable. You'll do, Liz Trent. We'll start the panto auditions on Tuesday.

Great! Thanks, Miss Wilson!

Monday came—

You should have seen Liz after her brush with Thunder . . . Ha! Ha!

Of course, Liz is clueless! I could have managed Thunder easily, but then I *DO* have a way with horses.

On the day of the auditions—

Right, Liz — start things rolling.

Okay, Miss Wilson. Everyone off the stage, please. We'll take you one at a time.

The End

79

My mother needs what I make selling lobsters to the hotels in the next town.

Oh yes, please! There's nobody left in the village who knows about boats. They've all gone to work in the town.

My grandpa might be able to help. He's good at repairing things. Shall I fetch him?

A little later—

It'll take a couple of days to repair this.

That's great! I'll use my old rowing boat meantime to collect lobsters.

While Grandpa worked, Jinny went with Joseph to get his lobster pots —

Not many lobsters today — just when I need extra money to pay your grandpa.

If you can give us a meal instead, that'll do fine.

So, later, Joseph took Jinny and Grandpa home —

The ship's figurehead? It came off my grandfather's boat. I'd like it on mine, but I don't know how to fix it.

You could do it, couldn't you, Grandpa?

Yes. It needs a bit of carving first, though. I'll see to it.

Inside the cottage— We've sat you in my grandfather's chair, Mr Jarvis. It's very old.

We have only plain fare, Jinny, but it's wholesome.

Next day— The salt water's got in and rusted the old engine. I don't know what I'll do now. I can't afford a new one — especially as I won't be able to take trippers out.

Will there be a trip round the lighthouse today?

Sorry, but there will be no more trips till I have my boat repaired.

Back at the caravan— Joseph says this figurehead is his lucky mascot.

He certainly needs some good luck.

Next day— I worry when Joseph's out in that old rowing boat. His father and grandfather were both drowned at sea. But if he doesn't keep the hotels supplied, they'll get their lobsters elsewhere.

Look! There he is! The boat's upturned!

Minutes later— The current will sweep him on to the rocks!

I'll fetch help!

I've hurt my arm! I can't swim!

84

A Monster

I thought I'd knit a rabbit
From a pattern in a book.
His colouring was very smart;
He had a trendy look.
I gathered all the balls of wool
And started at the head,
Quite sure that I could finish him
Before I went to bed.

The body grew and grew, and grew —
I thought he'd never stop —
The wool was finished, so I ran
Down to the corner shop.
I bought the wool and hurried back
To where I thought he lay . . .
But he had moved! I swear he'd grown
While I had been away!

No time for lunch, or even tea —
I didn't want to eat —
And it was nearly half-past-nine
Before I reached his feet.
I pressed him out and sewed him up,
Then I began to stuff —
I used the proper kind at first,
But there was not enough.

in wool

I seized on all that I could find,
Including Granny's hat.
The situation now was tense —
I even eyed the cat!
At midnight he was finished
(He was nothing like the book)
And when I sewed his features on,
Oh, what a crafty look!

I propped him up against the wall
And crept upstairs to bed —
But when I hurried down next day,
His stuffing he had shed!
It oozed between the stitches
Like an overcooked fruit pie —
But though all limp and lifeless,
He still had a crafty eye.

I put him in the dustbin,
Where he lay so limp and still
Like an out-of-work wool octopus . . .
It made me feel quite ill,
Almost guilty that I'd failed him,
For he'd only lived a day —
That jokey, crafty rabbit
That I had to throw away.

PENNY'S PONY

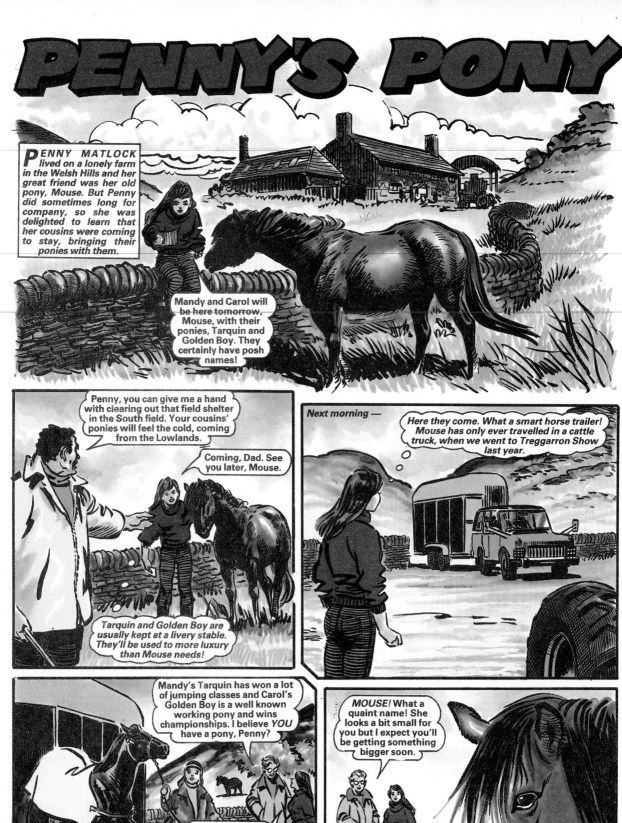

PENNY MATLOCK lived on a lonely farm in the Welsh Hills and her great friend was her old pony, Mouse. But Penny did sometimes long for company, so she was delighted to learn that her cousins were coming to stay, bringing their ponies with them.

Mandy and Carol will be here tomorrow, Mouse, with their ponies, Tarquin and Golden Boy. They certainly have posh names!

Penny, you can give me a hand with clearing out that field shelter in the South field. Your cousins' ponies will feel the cold, coming from the Lowlands.

Coming, Dad. See you later, Mouse.

Tarquin and Golden Boy are usually kept at a livery stable. They'll be used to more luxury than Mouse needs!

Next morning —

Here they come. What a smart horse trailer! Mouse has only ever travelled in a cattle truck, when we went to Treggarron Show last year.

Mandy's Tarquin has won a lot of jumping classes and Carol's Golden Boy is a well known working pony and wins championships. I believe *YOU* have a pony, Penny?

Er . . . yes, Aunt Caroline. That's Mouse in the field.

MOUSE! What a quaint name! She looks a bit small for you but I expect you'll be getting something bigger soon.

I . . . I don't know. Even Dad rides her when he's gathering sheep.

I don't expect a mountain pony would tire easily but she must be too small for a lot of classes at shows.

I . . . I don't go to many shows, Mandy.

I wouldn't want to change Mouse — I love her! But . . . but Mandy and Carol's ponies ARE rather nice looking.

I do hope your little pony won't kick ours. They ARE rather valuable.

Mouse never kicks.

The two ponies, freed, bucked spectacularly—

Do they always do that?

Of course — they can't be expected just to stand about like a rougher pony. All the same, I'm glad I'm not on Golden Boy at this minute!

Mouse decided that the display had gone on long enough and began to drive the two ponies down the field —

I see Mouse is sorting things out. The grazing is best down there. She'll soon have them settled and eating.

Oh, I see. The little pony wants to eat, so she's taking our two with her.

More likely Mouse thinks those two should graze and stop showing off.

Next day —

Uncle David says you'll show us the places to ride, Penny. I hope your little pony can keep up with our two.

Mouse is quite energetic, even if her legs are short.

But their lovely ponies will set a good pace. Perhaps they are right in a way when they say I'm getting too big for Mouse.

They won't come!

I expect it's because of Mouse! They're probably scared to come too near!

They're just being naughty! I wonder if they'll follow Mouse?

That's it, Mouse! Call them!

And soon the ponies were saddled and bridled —

Your little pony didn't like leaving ours, did she? She was calling to them.

I thought it was because she was telling them to behave!

Jenny took the track into the hills —

All right to canter? Tarquin's longing to go!

Yes . . . all right, but stop at the bridge. It's slippery.

Oh, Mouse, they're leaving us standing!

Steady! That bridge is slippery!

If they gallop on to that wooden bridge their ponies will fall. Dad told me always to WALK Mouse over it.

But Mandy and Carol did not intend to use the bridge —

Oh, Mouse, look at that!

93

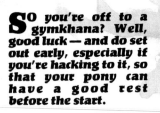

GYMKHANA

SO you're off to a gymkhana? Well, good luck — and do set out early, especially if you're hacking to it, so that your pony can have a good rest before the start.

When you arrive, unbox him straight away. If he has come a long journey, walk him about for a short time to relax him. Then rest him, tied up in the shade of a hedge or beneath a tree. Remember, he has plenty of work to do later.

Check early with the secretary, collect your numbers, enter any extra classes, and so on. If you have more than an hour to wait, give the pony a very small drink. Tidy him up with body-brush and duster — a soft linen cloth used to produce a shine on the coat. If necessary, plait mane and tail. For showing classes, smear a small amount of petroleum jelly around the edge of his eyes — it makes the eyes stand out, especially if they are on the small side. Oil his hooves.

Watch the sun. Your pony may not be in the shade for long, since it moves round — and you don't want a slow-roasted pony dripping with sweat in the showing class.

Never use the pony as a ringside seat.

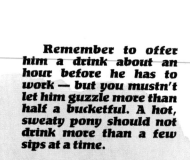

Remember to offer him a drink about an hour before he has to work — but you mustn't let him guzzle more than half a bucketful. A hot, sweaty pony should not drink more than a few sips at a time.

You should not gallop about between classes or let your friends ride him then. Once his classes are over, check him every half hour in case he gets loose, is kicked, or becomes caught up in his tie rope, haynet, or tack.

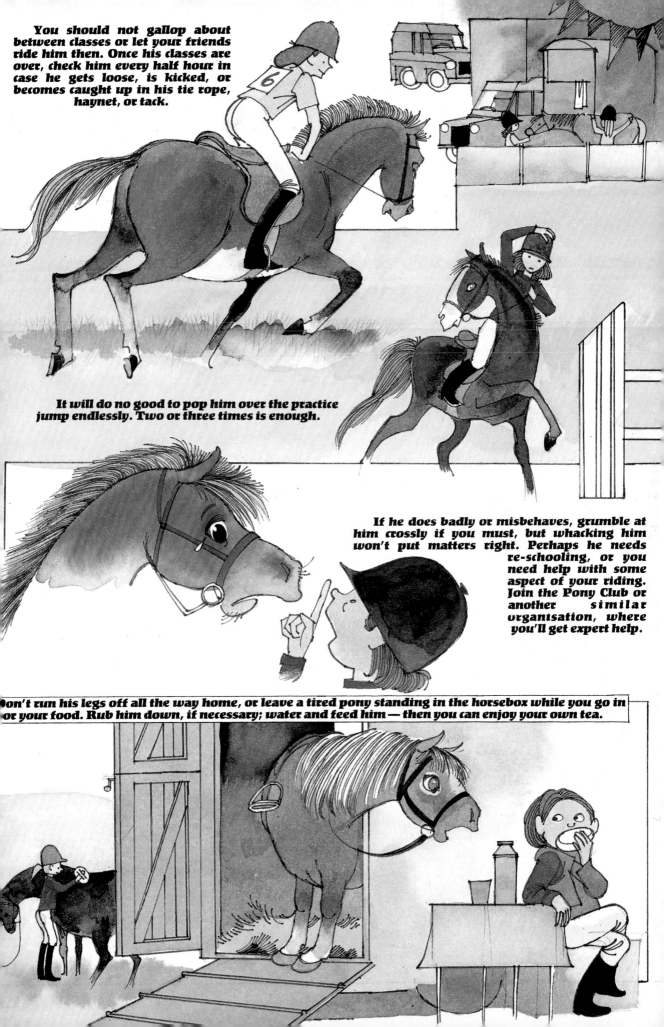

It will do no good to pop him over the practice jump endlessly. Two or three times is enough.

If he does badly or misbehaves, grumble at him crossly if you must, but whacking him won't put matters right. Perhaps he needs re-schooling, or you need help with some aspect of your riding. Join the Pony Club or another similar organisation, where you'll get expert help.

Don't run his legs off all the way home, or leave a tired pony standing in the horsebox while you go in for your food. Rub him down, if necessary; water and feed him — then you can enjoy your own tea.

The Treasure

INSIDE a tiny moorland cottage a woman lay so ill, that she didn't realise she had a visitor from the city . . .

I came as soon as I got the message, Nurse.

You're only just in time, Mrs Martin.

I've done all I can for the poor soul. There was nothing she wanted, except to have this old box where she could see it.

She tells me it's her treasure. Do you know what's in there?

Oh yes, indeed. It was Maggie's treasure that brought us together, so many years ago.

I was about thirteen when it happened. My mother was schoolmistress here in Ebbvale. Normally I was away at boarding school but at that particular time I was at home, recovering after an illness.

98

Then one day, when I called for Johnny...

What's this I hear about you two being seen near the abbey ruins? Old Seth was up there, looking for a lost sheep, and he saw you.

We weren't doing any harm, Dad.

I admit it's a great place for adventures. When I was a lad, me and some of my mates played "Knights of the Round Table" up there.

There was a big, flat stone in the cellars. That was our table. We used to hold proper meetings there just like the *REAL* knights would have done.

Don't encourage him, Sally. My dad will talk for hours about the old days.

Funny to think your dad and his friends used to come this way, to play in the ruins. That flat stone he mentioned must be the one where I give Maggie her reading lessons.

How much longer do we have to come trailing up here? It's a bit boring for me while you two are reading books.

But I can't let Maggie down now, Johnny. She's coming on really well.

Because Johnny was a bit huffy with me, we didn't speak for the last few yards of the journey. That was why Maggie didn't hear us coming —

Oh! You startled me!

What's that you just slipped down into that crack?

It's my treasure. I'm not showing it to anyone. You'll only want to take it away from me.

If I want to see it, I will! No girl's going to stop me.

102

Pepper the Pony

I've got a part in the school panto, Pepper.

CHOMP CHOMP

Not interested, eh? Suit yourself. My pals will be round shortly to rehearse.

Later—

Lucinda, where are you?

EH?

JEALOUS!

Lucinda?

That freak won't take MY place!

I think Pepper is angry!

Is he coming this way?

Yes! Run!

Now look what you've done! You've ruined our pantomime horse costume. What are we going to do?

Wait a minute. I've got it!

Bring on my trusty steed!

How embarrassing!

THE Gift Horse

CARRIE CLIFFORD had always loved horses although her parents could not afford to buy her a pony of her own. One morning, a letter arrived for Carrie.

It . . . it's from Auntie Alice, she says that she's been offered a job abroad. She needs a home for her pet pony and she's sending it to me, if you agree.

A pony? But Carrie, where on earth will you keep it?

Mr Richards has got a paddock. I could ask him.

If you can find a cheap place to keep it, I suppose you can try.

And so—

Yes, you can use the paddock, if you mend the fences and see to the water yourself.

Oh, thank you.

A pony of my own at last. Perhaps I'll be able to make proper friends with some of the pony-riding girls now.

Next day —

Hello. You're Carrie Clifford, aren't you? You sometimes ride at Mrs Gill's stables. Are you getting a pony or something?

Yes, I am. It's coming tomorrow. Mr Richards said I could use the paddock on condition I looked after the fences.

Great. Now you'll be able to come for rides with us. We can show you the bridle paths.

Thanks, I'd like that.

Next morning—

Carrie Clifford? Is this where you want the pony?

Oh, yes please.

But, Carrie was in for a shock—

Here he is then. Mind he doesn't trample on you. Ha! Ha!

B-But . . .

It's a Shetland . . . not a proper riding pony at all. So that's what Auntie Alice meant by 'pet pony'.

Oh, you're begging for me to give you something, aren't you? You may be tiny, but you are rather sweet.

Thank goodness Aunt Alice hadn't taken leave of her senses by sending you a pony after all, Carrie. I really think we might be able to afford to keep one this size.

But, a little later—

Oh no, is that it? The pony? Oh, really, what a laugh . . . just look at the size of it.

I don't think you'll be able to come riding with us on that, not unless you carry him. Ha! Ha!

Oh Hamish, they're laughing at you. Never mind, let them. I . . . I wish you could have been bigger, but you're still a pony, and I'll look after you.

So, it's a Sheltie you were getting. I've the very thing for this fellow. You come and see.

And so—

There you are! Mark my words lass, you'll never be bored with that fellow.

A cart. I never thought of driving. It would be fun.

And, quite soon—

Good boy, Hamish. That's the way.

Mr Richards said to take it slowly at first, but we'll try going out on the road tomorrow.

Next day—

Goodness! Look out, Lisa, it must be the fair.

Move over! Let the real ponies past.

Steady, Hamish.

And then—

Get that animal out of the way.

Hamish... go on...

Why did he have to choose that moment to be naughty?

Suddenly—

That branch — it would have fallen on us if Hamish hadn't stopped.

Or on us — steady pony, steady.

Do you know, I reckon that comic pony of yours may have saved us from a nasty accident.

Yes. I think he sensed something, and stopped because of the danger.

Carrie's right. Perhaps that shrimp isn't such a joke after all.

After they had moved the branch—

We'll see you soon, Carrie. 'Bye.

They've stopped laughing — thanks to Hamish's cleverness.

Two days later—

Help! Please help me!

Whoa, Hamish! I think that pony's in trouble.

Hang on. I'll bring Hamish.

He might help keep that pony calm while we untangle him.

It worked—

It's almost off. Oh, I'm so glad you came by. Jet was going spare — he'd have cut his leg to pieces if he'd gone on like that.

I'm glad we could help . . .

That's the second time Hamish has been able to help.

Next day—

Carrie! It's for you. Someone called Emma.

That's the name of the girl with the black pony that we helped yesterday.

And later—

Thank goodness. Jet just wouldn't settle down after that fright yesterday . . . I'm so glad I thought of asking Hamish to stay for a few days. Once Jet gets over his scare he'll be fine again. Maybe later I can ride with you and your cart for a bit, to settle him?

Why not? Hamish and I would enjoy that, I'm sure.

And they did—

He really can travel, can't he? That looks fun . . . they have cross-country driving competitions, you know. You should try them.

It IS fun . . . and Hamish likes it too. And what's more, I think I've found a friend in Emma.

On the way home—

What a lovely outfit. I wonder . . . could you come to the hospital fête with it tomorrow, to give rides to the children? They would so enjoy it.

I'd love to. Hamish will enjoy it too.

At the fête—

I like your little pony, miss, he's sweet.

You can pat him in a moment, and I'll show you his trick. He can 'ask' for titbits, you'll see.

Just then, Mr Richards came by—

You seem to have made lots of friends, lass. I reckon you don't regret getting this Sheltie now.

I certainly don't, Mr Richards. Hamish is great.

This lovely little pony has really changed my life.

THE END

109

CHRISTMAS BELLS

MELANIE ran along the lane, her long brown hair streaming out behind her. Even the mass of red berries on the holly tree shone with a new brilliance that morning as if they, too, knew that the impossible had happened!

Even now, with Derek's invitation in her hand, Melanie could hardly believe it. The most fantastic boy she had ever met had invited her to the Scouts' disco on Friday! And it wasn't as if she really knew him . . . not properly, that is.

Melanie slowed down as she reached the main road, and thought dreamily of the first time she had seen him, when Peter, her twin brother, had brought him home from Scouts and she had been half way down the garden path on her way to her friend, Jane's house.

Even though it had been dark she had known at once that there was something special about Derek. After that, she had seen him in the distance several times. Once he'd even smiled in her direction!

And now she knew for certain that he had really noticed her. Somehow it made her feel prettier and more alive. She couldn't wait to tell Jane about it.

At Guides last night there had been a Patrol Competition for designing and making an invitation for the Guides' own Christmas party.

"That's really great, Mel," Jane had said when she saw the one that Melanie had done. "You'll send it to Derek, won't you? Go on, Mel — I *DARE* you!

"Oh, no, I can't," Melanie had said, a tell-tale blush covering her cheeks. If only she had the courage to follow Jane's suggestion. All the time she had been painting the daintily shaded Christmas bells against the background of red and green holly, she had been thinking of Derek.

Jane would have sent *HER* card — but Jane was very confident. Melanie would only blush, and perhaps stammer like she sometimes did when she was nervous about something!

BUT today things were different, and Melanie smiled happily to herself.

Today she would send it to him because he had given her an invitation first.

Jane was looking very happy, too.

"You'll be going to the Scouts' disco, won't you, Jane?" Melanie asked, her eyes shining.

"Oh, yes, Pete was saying something about it. That's what gave me the . . . I mean, yes, I'll be going, Melanie," Jane replied.

Jane looked a little secretive, and smiled as if she knew something Melanie didn't know. But Melanie was writing her name on her invitation and didn't notice. She would ask Peter to give it to Derek at Scouts tonight.

Walking home with Jane after school, Melanie felt as if peals of Christmas bells were ringing out joyously all around her. She fingered Derek's invitation in her pocket.

"What will you wear?" asked Jane, smiling that secret smile again.

Melanie paused by the bridge over the stream . . . Perhaps Mum would let her get a new dress. Then she looked at Jane. There was something in her manner that was different.

"Why should Derek invite *ME*?" she said slowly. "I mean, he must know loads of girls. Why *ME*?"

Jane grinned at her maddeningly. "Why not? He's got to get to know you sometime," she answered.

A SUDDEN, terrible suspicion hit Melanie so hard that she gasped. "Jane, you DIDN'T . . .?" she asked breathlessly.

Jane looked rather sheepish.

"I only did it to help . . . so that you would invite him to our party and really get to know him," she muttered.

"Oh, Jane! Of all the mean, rotten things to do, sending an invitation supposed to be from Derek, to me!" Melanie cried.

She took out her hand-painted invitation to Derek, tore it into tiny little bits and threw it into the stream. Then she turned and ran as the tears rose in her eyes.

She must get home quickly and shut herself in her bedroom. No one must know . . . not Mum or Peter, or anyone! To think how near she had been to sending that invitation to Derek! She shivered to think of it, and felt hot and cold all at the same time. She would never speak to Jane again! Who needed enemies with HER as a best friend?

Jane avoided Melanie in school next day, but somehow, Melanie got through it, and walked slowly home on her own. Today no sunlight flickered on the holly berries in the lane, and Melanie hardly glanced at them as she passed. Who cared about holly when something like this had happened? She blinked rapidly as tears pricked her eyelids.

And then, suddenly, incredibly, Derek was there with two thick gloves in one hand and a pair of secateurs in the other.

"Oh, hello," he said, giving her a shy smile and his brown eyes lit up with a kind of warmth.

"Oh," she gasped.

Derek flushed slightly, and waved the secateurs.

"I've come for some holly for the disco tomorrow. I'm glad there's some left," he said.

Melanie glanced vaguely at the holly and then back at him. If only she could think of something rivetting to say so that he wouldn't just walk away. Jane would have thought of something. At the thought of Jane, her so-called friend, Melanie felt her face flood with colour. Thank goodness she had discovered Jane's little trick in time.

"We always get holly at the last minute for our Christmas discos," he was saying. "Then on Saturday we take it round to the Old People's Home . . . You know, Broadlands House up on the main road. So we need it really fresh. It's good fun decorating the place for them. We do it every year," he smiled.

"The holly's really beautiful this year," said Melanie.

"This year's special because Mr Young will be a hundred years old on Christmas Day. His wife lives there, too, but she's only eighty five," Derek replied.

"ONLY!" said Melanie, thinking about it.

Derek laughed. "Strange, isn't it? She was seventy years old when I was born, and he was . . ."

"Eighty five," said Melanie in wonder. She wanted to ask him if Mr Young and his wife had always lived round here. Perhaps they had walked down this lane when they were young, and seen the holly.

ALL at once there seemed a lot to talk to him about.

"Would you like to come and help decorate?" he asked. "And you'll come to the disco, won't you, Melanie?"

She looked at him, and felt suddenly breathless.

"You see," he went on, "I wanted to ask you before, but I was afraid that you would say 'no'. Then, this morning, when your invitation came . . ."

"MY invitation?" Melanie gasped.

"To the Guide party," Derek replied and pulled the card out of his pocket. "It IS yours, isn't it?"

Melanie glanced at the daintily shaded bells against their background of holly, and nodded. "Yes," she said faintly. "It's mine, Derek."

"It sort of gave me confidence," Derek said. "So I thought I'd try this lane for holly, hoping I'd meet you."

He smiled at her warmly, and she knew he really meant it.

And after she had helped him cut the holly she would go straight round to Jane's house. Trust Jane to do something so incredibly marvellous! She'd copied her invitation and her signature and made sure Derek got it! No one could possibly have a better friend than Jane!

The End

111

Barker spotted the toe-joints—

He lifted one, then made for the door—

BARKER!

What? Oh, no!

But Barker had disappeared—

He'll have taken it somewhere to bury it. I *AM* sorry, Phil.

No time to waste being sorry — we've got to get that bone back.

They searched all Barker's favourite burying places—

Nothing! And he sits there looking so smug. Oh, Barker. you are naughty.

Bring that spade over here, will you?

A few minutes later—

Phil is really angry.

Nothing here, either. Let me talk to that dog!

Where's the bone, Barker? *BONE!* Now, look here, you find that bone, understand? Come on — *FIND IT!*

It's no use talking to Barker like that. He doesn't like being shouted at.

They followed Barker into the hall—

The plant! He's . . .

Sshh! Don't disturb him.

Good boy, Barker.

Right! Now let's get this bone back to the museum.

Later—

Well, that's the bone safely back. Do cheer up, Phil. It could have been a lot worse.

On their way home, Phil remained silent—

Just my luck. Phil's the most interesting boy I've ever met, but he really is very moody.

I'm leaving you here, Mandy.

Yes, I thought you would.

116

ABC of LOVE

Love can be as easy as A,B,C. If you don't believe me — read on!

A An August afternoon —

B But bother's brewing —

C

COR!

D Dave doesn't dig Diane's dreams . . .

E . . . 'e's exceedingly . . .

121

WILD FLOWER TRAIL

START

U	D	N	I	W	H	E	S	F	L
K	G	A	O	J	S	U	N	Z	B
S	E	C	I	F	L	D	P	O	X
S	D	S	B	T	I	E	L	I	O
O	Y	B	U	P	T	R	L	V	L
Q	R	A	D	P	E	E	E	P	C
Z	M	I	R	A	B	R	O	U	P
I	L	E	D	N	E	P	C	B	Y
O	R	O	W	M	Q	U	L	G	H
N	X	H	S	E	V	I	R	J	T

FINISH

Can you find your way through the maze of wild flowers? You can move forwards, backwards, up, down or diagonally. Letters may be used more than once.

1. DAISY
2. BUTTERCUP
3. CLOVER
4. POPPY
5. BLUEBELL
6. VIOLET
7. PRIMROSE
8. COWSLIP
9. DANDELION
10. ROSE

SOLUTION —

FINISH

START

122

Pumpk

I left my house on Friday
With a pumpkin in my hand,
I crossed the road and took a bus
To Simpson's, in the Strand.

I walked into the kitchen
And I called out for the chef,
But no-one seemed to hear me —
Were they really all stone deaf?

I offered them my pumpkin,
Said I'd like to have it fried.
They didn't have a pumpkin pan,
So back I went outside.

I took it to the fried-fish shop
And eyed the bubbling fat,
But Harry stared and shouted, "Wow!
Just what on earth is that?"

I rushed outside, offended;
No-one else could really know
All the trouble I had taken
Just to get the thing to grow.

Then, walking through St James's Park,
Some boys called: "Look! That's weird!
'Twould make a smashing football
Now that ours has disappeared!"

I wasn't going to tell them
That it wouldn't bounce at all,
And one kick sent it sailing high
Across the Palace wall.

I hope the Queen's enjoying it
With bacon — nice and lean —
Perhaps I'll be appointed
"Pumpkin Grower to the Queen"!

click!

JUDY CAPTURES THE FUN ON FILM . . .